Hercules

re-told by
Brandon Robshaw

Published in association with
The Basic Skills Agency

Hodder & Stoughton

A MEMBER OF THE HODDER HEADLINE GROUP

Acknowledgements
Cover: Fred van Deelen
Illustrations: Mike Bell

Orders; please contact Bookpoint Ltd, 39 Milton Park, Abingdon, Oxon OX14 4TD. Telephone: (44) 01235 400414, Fax: (44) 01235 400454. Lines are open from 9.00–6.00, Monday to Saturday, with a 24 hour message answering service. Email address: orders@bookpoint.co.uk

British Library Cataloguing in Publication Data
A catalogue record for this title is available from the British Library

ISBN 0 340 77511 4

First published 2000
Impression number 10 9 8 7 6 5 4 3 2 1
Year 2005 2004 2003 2002 2001 2000 1999

Typeset by GreenGate Publishing Services, Tonbridge, Kent.
Printed in Great Britain for Hodder and Stoughton Educational, a division of Hodder Headline Plc, 338 Euston Road, London NW1 3BH, by Atheneum Press, Gateshead, Tyne & Wear

Hercules

Contents

Snakes 1

A Fit of Madness 3

The Nemean Lion 5

The Hydra and the Deer
with the Golden Horns 8

The Wild Boar of the Mountains
and the Stables of King Augeas 11

The Birds of Brass and the
Mad Bull of Crete 14

The Wild Horses of King Diomedes 17

The Amazons and the
Mighty Ogre, Geryon 19

Three Golden Apples 23

The Hound of Hell 27

Introduction

The story of Hercules
was told in ancient Greece
over three thousand years ago.

The twelve labours
were twelve difficult tasks.

These were given to Hercules as a punishment
for a crime he committed
whilst under a spell from
his enemy, Hera, Zeus's queen.

Snakes

When Hercules was a baby, he killed two snakes.
They came gliding into his room one night.
They came straight for him.
Their mouths opened wide.

Most babies would have cried or screamed,
but not Hercules.
He grabbed the snakes by the neck.
They hissed and wriggled,
trying to bite him.
Hercules squeezed with all his strength.
Soon, the two huge snakes lay dead.
He had strangled them.
He was only ten months old.

This was the first sign that Hercules
was no ordinary child.
When his parents saw what he had done,
they were amazed.

His mother went to see Tiresias.
Tiresias was the wisest man
in the city of Thebes.
He was blind, very old and he could see into the future.

'There's something strange
about my boy Hercules,' said his mother.
The old blind man nodded.
'He is the son of Zeus –
the King of the Gods.'

'But – how can that be?'

'Zeus came to you one night
when your husband was away.
He was in disguise.
You thought it was your husband,
but Zeus is Hercules's true father.

'Because of this,
Hera, Zeus's Queen, is jealous.
It was Hera
who sent those snakes against him.
She will always be his enemy,
but Hercules
will become the greatest hero in all Greece.'

A Fit of Madness

Hercules grew up tall and strong.
He learned to box and wrestle.
He was a deadly shot with a bow and arrow.

When still a young man,
he killed a lion with his club.
He stripped its skin off.
After that, he always wore the skin
around his shoulders.

Hercules got married and had three sons.
It looked as if he was going
to have a happy, peaceful life.
Until Hera, Queen of the Gods,
stepped in.
By her magic powers,
she sent Hercules mad.

Hercules was sitting on a hillside,
watching his three sons play.
Suddenly, madness took over his mind.
He thought his sons were enemies.
He jumped to his feet.
He picked up his bow and arrow.

He shot three arrows
and every one found its mark.
His three boys lay dead.

Then Hercules came back to his senses.
He stared in horror at what he had done.

It wasn't Hercules's fault he'd gone mad,
so he was not put to death for his crime.
Still, he had to be punished.

He was sent to be the slave
of his cousin Eurystheus.
He would have to do ten Labours for him.
Only then would Hercules be free again.

The Nemean Lion

Eurystheus was the King of Tiryns.
He was the same age as Hercules
but he was not like him at all.
Eurystheus was weak and a coward.
Like Hera, he hated Hercules.
'Your first Labour,' he told Hercules,
'is to go and kill the Nemean Lion.'

Hercules had already killed one lion,
but the Nemean lion was a bit different.
It was a huge creature
with a hide as hard as iron.
It killed cattle and people.
No one could stop it.

Hercules tracked it to its cave.
The bones of cattle and people
lay all around.
The lion saw Hercules.
It licked its lips.
It crouched, ready to spring.
Hercules fired an arrow at it
but the arrow just bounced off.

He ran at the lion and struck it
with his sword,
but the sword broke
against the lion's iron-hard hide.

The lion roared.
Hercules hit it with his club.
The club just bounced off.
No weapon could kill the lion
but perhaps sheer strength could.
Hercules grabbed the lion by the neck.
They rolled over and over,
struggling on the ground.
The lion bit off one of Hercules's fingers.
He ignored the pain.
He squeezed harder,
choking the life out of the lion.
At last, it lay dead.

Hercules carried the body back.
He threw it down in front of Eurystheus. 'There's
your lion,' he said.
'Take the nasty thing away!' said Eurystheus.
'Well, you won't find the next Labour so easy.
Go and kill the Hydra!'

The Hydra and the Deer with the Golden Horns

The Hydra was a terrible monster.
It was a giant snake with nine heads.
The middle head could not die.
Its breath was poisonous.
It lived in the marshes.
Hercules took along his nephew, Iolaus.
'Light me a fire,' he said.
'When you see the Hydra, hold your breath.'

Hercules lit one of his arrows at the fire.
He shot it into the Hvdra's cave.
The Hydra came out, hissing angrily.
Hercules smashed one of its heads
with his club.
At once, two more heads
grew in its place.

Iolaus ran to help.
He took a burning stick from the fire.
Every time Hercules smashed a head,

Iolaus burned the stump.
This stopped more heads growing.

Soon, there was only the middle head left –
the one that could never die.
Hercules cut it off with his sword.
Iolaus burned the stump.
Then Hercules buried the head under a rock.
The battle was over.

Hercules went back to Eurystheus
and told him what he had done.
'That Labour doesn't count!'
said Eurystheus. 'Your nephew helped you.
Now, go and bring me
the Deer with the Golden Horns.'

The Deer with the Golden Horns
wandered free over the hills of Greece.
It ran so fast, it took Hercules a year
to catch it.
At last he caught up with it.
Without harming the beautiful animal,
he took it back to Eurystheus.

'You took your time,' said Eurystheus.
'Now you can go and do something
a bit more dangerous.
Bring me the Wild Boar of the Mountains – alive!'

The Wild Boar of the Mountains and the Stables of King Augeas

The Wild Boar of the Mountains
was a huge beast.
Its tusks were as sharp as razors.
It was so fierce, no one dared go near it.

Except Hercules.
He chased it around the mountain
until it fell into a snow-drift.
He jumped in after it.
He tied its legs together.
Then he carried the huge beast
back to Eurystheus.

Eurystheus was so scared,
he jumped into a large brass pot.
'Take it away!' he said.
'I'm not coming out until it's gone!'

Hercules took the Boar to the sea.
He untied its legs and watched it swim away.
Then he went back to Eurystheus.
'Now what?' he asked.

'Oh, I've thought of a lovely job,'
said Eurystheus.
'Go and clean out the stables of King Augeas.'
He laughed.
'They haven't been cleaned
for thirty years,
so you'll find it a bit smelly!'

So Hercules went off to King Augeas.
'If I clean your stables in one day,'
said Hercules, 'what will you give me?'
'A tenth of all my cattle,' said King Augeas.

'It's a deal,' said Hercules.
He dug a channel from a nearby river
to the stables.
The river rushed down the channel
and through the stables.
They were cleaned out in no time.

Hercules felt quite pleased with himself,
but King Eurystheus was not impressed.
'That one doesn't count.
You got paid for it.
He gave you some of his cattle.
You're supposed to be a slave.
Slaves don't get paid.
Now go and chase away the Birds of Brass.'

The Birds of Brass and the Mad Bull of Crete

The Birds of Brass were nasty creatures.
They had wings, claws and beaks of brass.
Their beaks were strong enough
to pierce armour.
They ate human flesh

Hercules got rid of them quite easily.
He went to the woods where they lived.
He rattled a pair of brass castanets.
The noise was so loud,
the birds flew away in fear.
Hercules shot some of them down
as they flew.

He took them to Eurystheus.
'That was too easy,' said Eurystheus.
He kicked the dead birds away.
'Go and do something hard.
Bring me the Mad Bull of Crete.'

Hercules took a ship to the island of Crete.
The King of Crete was only too glad
to let him have the bull.
'It's a terror, that bull,' he said.
'Please take it away – if you can!'

Hercules could, of course.
He grabbed the bull by the horns
and carried it onto his ship.
He took it back to Eurystheus.

As soon as the Mad Bull saw Eurystheus,
it went for him.
Eurystheus only just jumped
into his brass pot in time.
He hid there until the bull had gone.

'Right,' he said to Hercules.
'Your next Labour is to bring me
the Wild Horses of King Diomedes.
Make sure you tame them
before you bring them back.
They're maneaters!'

The Wild Horses of King Diomedes

King Diomedes was not a nice man.
He had a habit of throwing his guests
to his four wild horses to be eaten.

He pretended to be friendly to Hercules,
but Hercules didn't trust him.
He knew it was dangerous to hang around.
He stole the four horses.
One of Diomedes' servants helped.
He opened the stable door for Hercules.

Hercules tied the wild horses to his chariot.
Then he left.
The servant came with him.

They hadn't gone far
when Hercules saw they were being followed.
Diomedes was following with his soldiers.
The servant had double-crossed Hercules.
He'd warned Diomedes about the escape.

Hercules stopped.
He left the horses.

He ran back to deal with the soldiers.
He broke down the sea wall.
The sea rushed through
and drowned the soldiers.

Hercules captured Diomedes.
He took him back to his chariot.
There, he found that the horses
had eaten the servant.
Hercules threw Diomedes to the horses
and they ate him too.

Hercules took the horses
back to Eurystheus.
On the way, he tamed them.
They never ate anyone after that.

There was no rest for Hercules.
Eurystheus sent him to get the belt
of the Queen of the Amazons.

The Amazons and the Mighty Ogre, Geryon

The Amazons were a race of
warlike women.
They fought with swords and spears.
Every Amazon cut off her right breast
so she could draw her bow more easily.
No men were allowed in their country.

Hercules took a ship.
With nine companions,
he sailed to the country of the Amazons.

Hercules was expecting a fight.
To his surprise,
the Queen of the Amazons was friendly.
She met him at the port.
He told her why he had come.
She offered to give him her belt.

The goddess Hera was watching.
She thought Hercules was getting off
too easily.
So she disguised herself as an Amazon.
She went to the Amazon city.

‘Pirates are attacking us!’ she said.

The Amazons grabbed their weapons.
They ran down to the port
to fight Hercules and his men.

There was a fierce battle.
At last, Hercules captured
the Queen’s sister.
‘Give us the belt!’ he said to the Queen.
‘Or your sister’s had it!’

The Queen handed over her belt.
Hercules and his men
sailed away as fast as they could.

Eurystheus gave the belt to his daughter.
Then he sent Hercules off on his next Labour –
to bring back the cattle of Geryon.

Geryon was a mighty ogre.
He had three heads and six arms.
He wasn’t too happy
when Hercules came to take his cattle.
Each of his six hands grabbed a weapon.
‘I’ll smash you to pieces!’ he said.

Even Hercules didn’t fancy a fight
with this monster.
So he raised his bow and fired three arrows.

The arrows went through
Geryon's three necks
and that was the end of him.

Hercules took the cattle back
to Eurystheus.
'There – that's ten Labours,' he said.
'I've finished.'

'Oh no, you haven't,' said Eurystheus.
'Two labours didn't count.
You had help with one
and got paid for another.
You've got two more to do.
Bring me three Golden Apples from the Garden of
the Hesperides!'

Three Golden Apples

Hercules didn't have a clue
where to find the Golden Apples.
He wandered around, searching.
On his travels,
he met a huge man chained to a rock.

The man was Prometheus.
Many years before,
he had stolen fire from the Gods,
to give to man.
Zeus punished him
by chaining him to the rock.
Every day, a vulture flew down
and pecked his liver out.

Hercules took pity on Prometheus
and freed him.
In return, Prometheus told him
how to get the Golden Apples.

'They're in a magic garden in North Africa.
You can't go in. Humans are not allowed.
Near there, you will find my brother, Atlas.

He is a giant, who stands on top of a mountain,
holding up the sky.
He will get the apples for you.'

Hercules went on his way.
He found Atlas,
standing on top of the mountain.
'I'll get the Golden Apples for you,' said Atlas,
'if you kill the snake that guards the tree.'

Hercules saw a great snake,
coiled around the tree in the garden.
He raised his bow and shot.
The arrow hit the snake in the head.
It crawled away to die.

'Now' said Atlas,
'can you hold up the sky while I'm gone?'

Hercules took the sky on his shoulders.
Atlas went striding down the mountain
towards the Garden of the Hesperides.

A day passed.
The sky pressed down heavily
on Hercules's shoulders.
Then he saw Atlas striding back.

He held three Golden Apples.

'Thanks!' said Hercules.
'Now you can take the sky back!'

'No, I don't want to,' said Atlas.
'I'm fed up with it. I need a holiday.'

This worried Hercules.
What if the giant left him there forever?
He thought quickly.
'All right,' he said.
'I'll carry on holding up the sky
if you just show me the best way to hold it.'

'All right,' said Atlas.
'Like this, see?'
He took the sky on his shoulders again.

'Yes,' said Hercules.
'You know, you do it so well,
I think I'll leave it to you.'

Hercules walked away,
juggling the three Golden Apples.

The Hound of Hell

Hercules' last Labour was the worst of all.
Eurystheus sent him to get
the Three-Headed Hound of Hell.

Hercules set off.
He went into a cave in the mountains
and climbed down, down, down.
He came to the River Styx –
a dark, gloomy underground river.
Across it lay Hell.
The ferryman took Hercules across.

Hercules found himself in a sad,
twilight world.
White ghosts drifted about, moaning.
He saw dead souls
being tortured for their crimes in life.

At last, he found the Hound of Hell
by the banks of the Styx.
It rushed at him,
its three great mouths open wide.

Hercules grabbed the Hound.
He wrestled it to the ground.

It was a terrible fight.
The Hound bit and scratched
and struggled.
In the end, Hercules was too strong.
The Hound gave up the struggle.

Hercules carried the Hound
back to Eurystheus.
‘Here!’ he said. ‘I’ve done itl’

The Hound barked madly
and ran at Eurystheus.
Just in time, Eurystheus jumped
into his brass pot.

‘That’s all my Labours done,’
said Hercules.
‘Yes!’ screamed Eurystheus.
‘Just take that monster away!’

Hercules carried the Hound
back down to Hell.
He came back to the sunlight
empty-handed.
His Labours had taken twelve years.
At last they were over.
He was a free man.